Sam
The Quarry Fox

Photography by David S V Lewis

Story by Angela M H Lewis

First Printing 2020

ISBN 978-1-5272-5542-5

Published by
David Lewis
davidsvlewis@outlook.com

Printed in the United Kingdom by
BWW Print Limited, Bridgwater

I am a wild fox who was born in the Old Town Quarry, Weston-super-Mare, next to Weston Woods, the quarry is used as an Arts Centre, a very peaceful venue and popular with visitors.

I am one of a litter of five, the others moved on but I decided,to stay, there is always food to be found and plenty of undergrowth to hide in if needed. When very young I mostly explored during the late evening and night but now wander around at any time, I know all my safe areas and the quarry is definitely one of the best.

I always follow my special person as soon as I see him, he puts food in some really strange places sometimes, then I hear a clicking sound but don't mind so long as my favourite food is on offer!

This is my story in photographs.

This is me aged around six months and the first time I heard the strange sound. I continued to be careful staying a safe distance away from everyone during the day but eventually became much braver.

I often leave the quarry for a while to explore elsewhere (obeying my nature) but I always come back.

I feel safe here, expecially in the evenings when all the visitors
have left.

There are some very strange things around today, I can't work out what this is, it was definitely not here yesterday!

Why would a tree be in here?

Now it's gone...

...and here it is again, looking different – all very confusing.

This is something I've never seen before, wonder where it all comes from.

I'll sit here and think about it!

My first set of cubs were born in the quarry, there were four all together, here we are having some extra food.

Can these two have a bit more?

A couple of inquisitive cubs – they are always first out of the den.

A peaceful afternoon, it must be a Monday or Tuesday – no
visitors around.

▶️ **YouTube** Search for *Sam the Quarry Fox (four of her cubs playing)*

18

The cubs are growing up fast.

Now meet George, he arrived in the quarry one evening and started to play with my cubs, he was on his own and posed no threat so I let him stay. He looked slightly younger than my litter (probably an orphan) and seemed quite determined that I adopt him – oh well, one more won't make much difference!

This is Kerry (one of the inquisitives). She spends most of her time with me.

The cubs always enjoy a game of hide and seek.

Foxes don't usually sunbathe but it was such a nice day, all the cubs were off exploring so I decided to have a pleasant relaxing afternoon.

This is my special feeding place – I'm very gentle. I know we have a reputation for sometimes being dangerous but how we behave depends in general on the situation we find ourselves in.

▶ YouTube Search for *Sam the Quarry Fox (feeding Sam while sitting)*

Kerry sits here quite often, maybe she likes the scent of the flowers!

A few months later one by one my cubs decided to leave home, Kerry stayed around for a little longer but even she decided to go off and find her own territory eventually. Not George – my adopted cub decided that the quarry was going to be his home – probably because he had arrived from elsewhere.

It eventually became obvious that George was not feeling well, he looked thinner and his fur began to fall out. My special person said George would have to be caught and taken to a place called 'Secret World Wildlife Rescue' where they look after sick animals and give them treatment.

Within a few days George was caught and taken away, he probably didn't like travelling in a vehicle but it was for his own good.

Okay if I get in and have a look?

What are all these?

Now they've disappeared and I was only gone for a few minutes!

I think I can smell something here, it might be food.

Let's have a go at getting it out.

Now this is really strange, that fox I can see doesn't move.

This is not moving either, I know it usually does because I often watch from a distance.

I still enjoy investigating everything in sight but not feeling too well now, probably have the same condition as George so expect to be taken to the same place.

I was right, my person persuaded me to come inside the building for some food and then tried to get me into a cage – I was not too keen at first and wandered around looking at everything for a while but all the doors were shut so I sat down and waited. Then the smell of my very favourite meat began to reach me, it was inside the cage so thought I might as well go in and eat it!

Very soon I was on my way to Secret World.

They put me in a compound with George, he seemed happy to see me and we stayed together. My person came to visit and brought my favourite food, I didn't mind being there and began to feel better but hoped I could soon go home.

Secret World
Wildlife Rescue

Pauline and Derek Kinder founded Secret World (or Bluebell Sett as it was then known) in 1992 to support wildlife work and were recognised nationally by winning the BBC Animal Country Award in 1995. The name was originally chosen to honour '*Bluebell*' one of the first badger cubs reared by Pauline. After release, although free to go the badger decided to stay, she then raised two cubs of her own, also adopting three others.

Their aim is to rescue, treat, rehabilitate and release animals back into the wild. Their vision is to inspire in everyone a love of British wildlife and of the countryside.

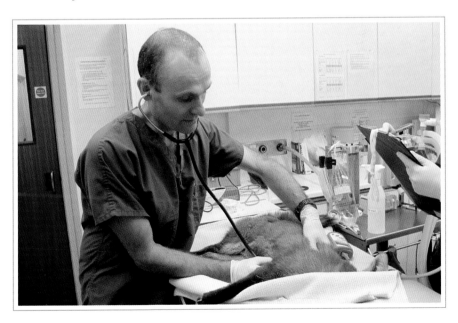

George and I stayed in Secret World for a few weeks having our treatment, then for the journey home we were placed in separate cages and put into a vehicle. Both of us were very excited on approaching the quarry – now we knew where we were!

George was released first and raced away as fast as possible up the side path, through the undergrowth and into the woods. I took my time, looked around for a few minutes, then followed George.

George raced off into the undergrowth.

▶ YouTube Search for *Sam the Quarry Fox (release)*

I stayed away for at least two or three weeks checking my territory, I had to make sure that everything was okay because eventually somewhere safe would be needed for my second set of cubs. We always choose a different location for each litter. George, being male, had no such interest and within a day or two returned to the quarry.

George returns to the quarry.

This is when I decided to come back, it was early one evening with no one around so I sat and waited for my special person – very relaxing after all that rushing about in the woods!

George and I had caught '*mange*' – it would have killed us without treatment. We are better now but I still have this bald patch, hope the fur soon grows again.

Quarry Visitors' Book signed by
Martin Hughes-Games
Zoologist, Natural History Programme Producer
and well known for co-presenting the BBC series
Spring Watch and its spin-offs.
Martin is also a patron of
Secret World Wildlife Rescue.

Name	email Address
MARTIN HUGHES-GAMES	M Hyles Jaes.

4 excellent days in the Quarry - inspecting the Rock & dropping off the cliffs - to the accompaniment of the croaking Ravens, Scolding Peregines - a buzzard + even a glimpse of the legadory "Quarry fox" A little Wildlife haven on the edge of Weston-Super-mare - delightful!!

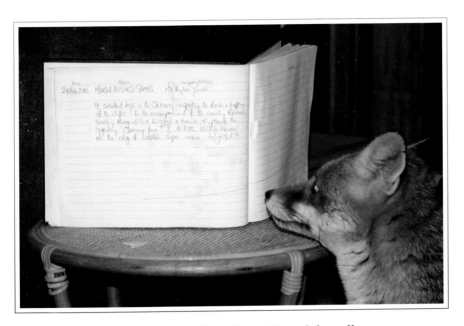

This looks interesting, a lot of people read it and they all seem very pleased.

George stayed for a while after my return but eventually decided that it was time to leave, my adopted cub had grown up and obviously now wanted his own territory. I occasionally caught sight of him in the woods but he never returned to the quarry.

George decides to leave.

Any more?

It's been raining, I prefer to drink from puddles whenever possible.

We don't want a return of mange so having medication drops on my neck, they don't bother me at all, I'm far too busy eating.

▶ **YouTube** Search for *Sam the Quarry Fox (mange treatment)*

The Old Town Quarry held a fundraising event for Secret World Wildlife Rescue

Meet two of my second set of cubs, I've brought them from the woods to visit the quarry. They must learn all about their environment and surrounding area.

This one seems a bit hesitant about coming down.

I've been away for a while but had a fight, my mouth is injured so came back very quickly to the quarry.

Antiseptic cream obtained from Secret World to treat Sam's mouth injury.

▶ YouTube Search for *Sam the Quarry Fox (treating injury)*

Just having a little nap but thought I heard something.

Yes I did, someone must have arrived on this.

My mouth feels a lot better now.

I remember this cold white stuff.

It's very strange and tastes a bit like water.

▶ YouTube Search for *Sam the Quarry Fox (sam and snowman)*

What was that?

▶ YouTube Search for *Sam the Quarry Fox (Sam on bench)*

So this is me!

I enjoy my exploring days but this is my favourite time –
when the woods and the quarry change and daylight
fades away, we hunt in the dark and defend our territory.
The night world becomes ours and it then belongs
only to us – until the sunrise.

Getting to spend so much time with a wild
animal has been a truly amazing experience,
having such trust enabled me to treat her
injuries and also protect her from mange.

One of my best experiences was when she
sat next to me while her cubs played in the grass,
I would often put chicken in particularly unusual
places to get pictures of her, she was probably
the most photographed fox in Weston!

I hope you have enjoyed this book
about Sam the Quarry Fox and
the time that she spent with me.

David

Wild animals should always be treated with care and caution.

▶ YouTube Sam Quarry Fox

The Old Town Quarry
South Road
Weston-super-Mare
North Somerset
BS23 2LS

Website **www.oldtownquarry.co.uk**